WHAT MAKES YOU BEAUTIFUL

by Sherry Selley

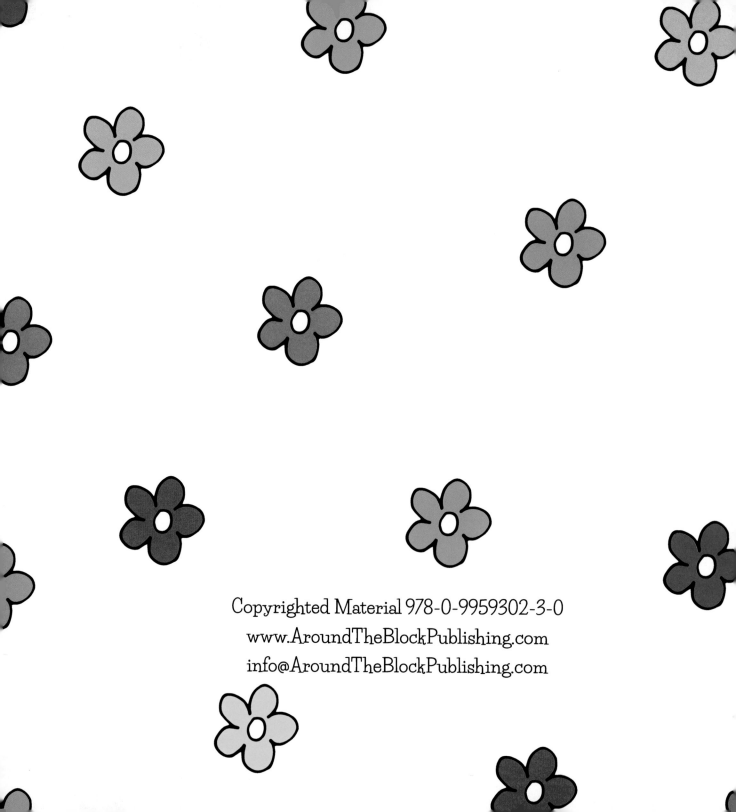

www.AroundTheBlockPublishing.com
info@AroundTheBlockPublishing.com

"When you are beautiful

on the inside it shows

on the outside".

- Sherry Selley -

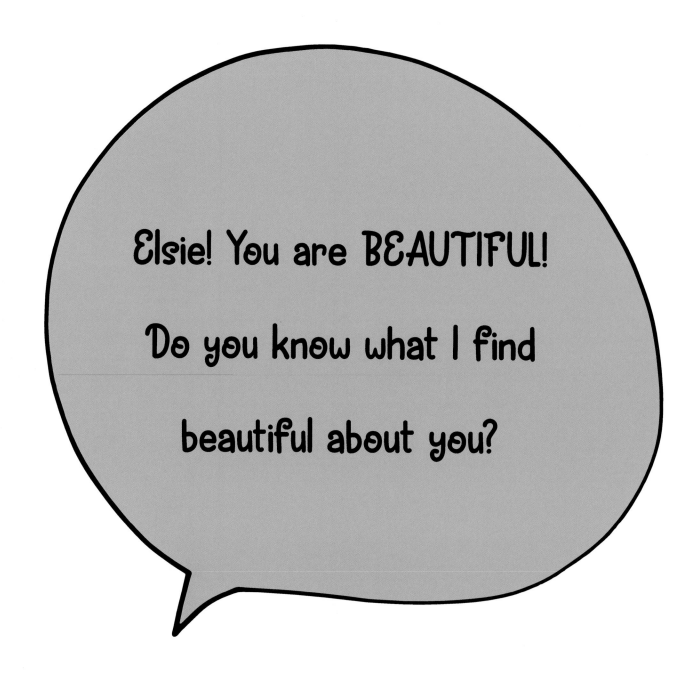

My new flower patterned

TWIRLY DRESS is beautiful.

Is THAT what it is?

Nope. While your new flower patterned twirly dress is INDEED very nice, that is NOT what makes you beautiful.

My brown leather

BOOTS are beautiful,

is THAT why?

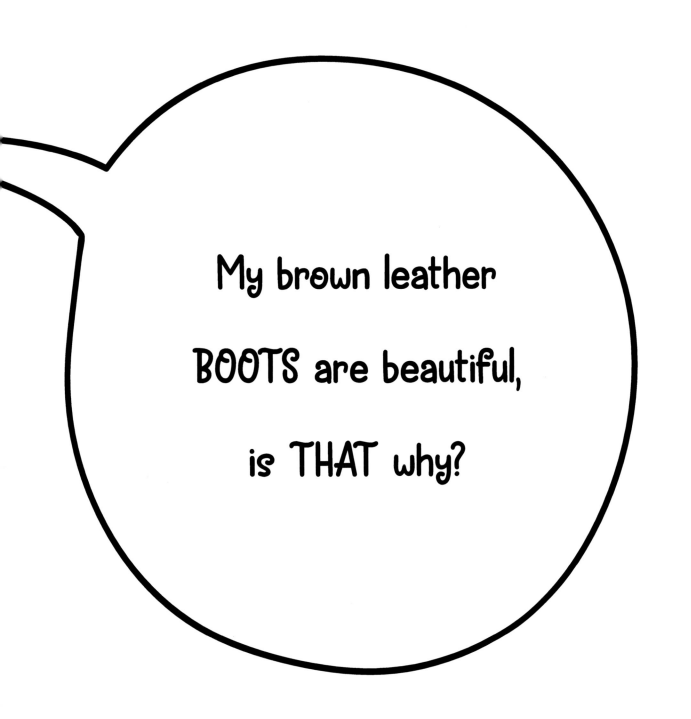

WOW! Those are some VERY nice boots! But no, that is NOT what makes you beautiful.

OH!!! I think I've got it! It must be my PINK STRAWBERRY SPARKLE LIP GLOSS that you find beautiful!

Your pink strawberry sparkle lip gloss is lovely (and smells GREAT!) But NOPE. That is NOT what makes you beautiful.

Hmmmm... is it my FULL VOLUME MIDNIGHT BLACK FALSE EYELASHES???

WOWZERS! Those are some IMPRESSIVE lashes! But nope, that is NOT what makes you beautiful.

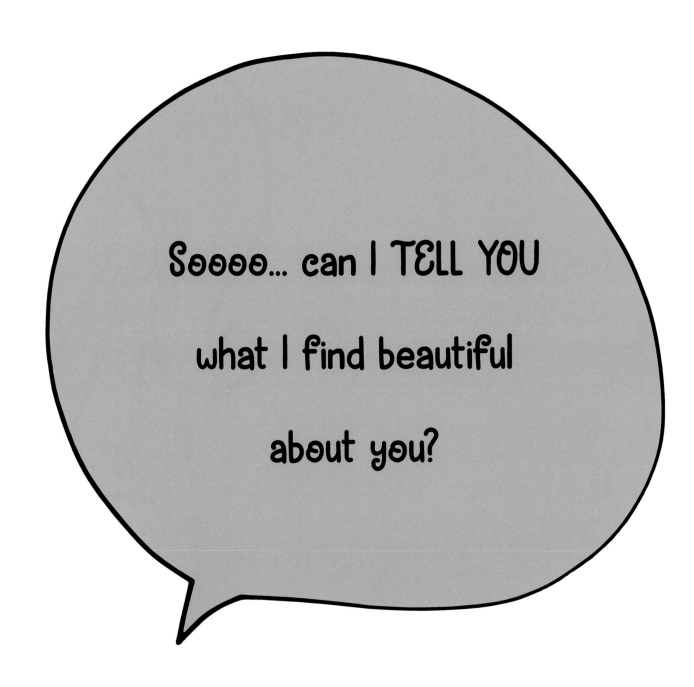

You are beautiful because

you have a beautiful HEART

and you always make me

feel loved!

You are beautiful because

you have a beautiful MIND!

I love listening to all your

AMAZING ideas!

You are beautiful because

you have a beautiful VOICE

that says kind words like

"Can I help you?"

You are beautiful because

you have beautiful ENERGY

and people can feel it when

they are around you!

WOW! THANKS!

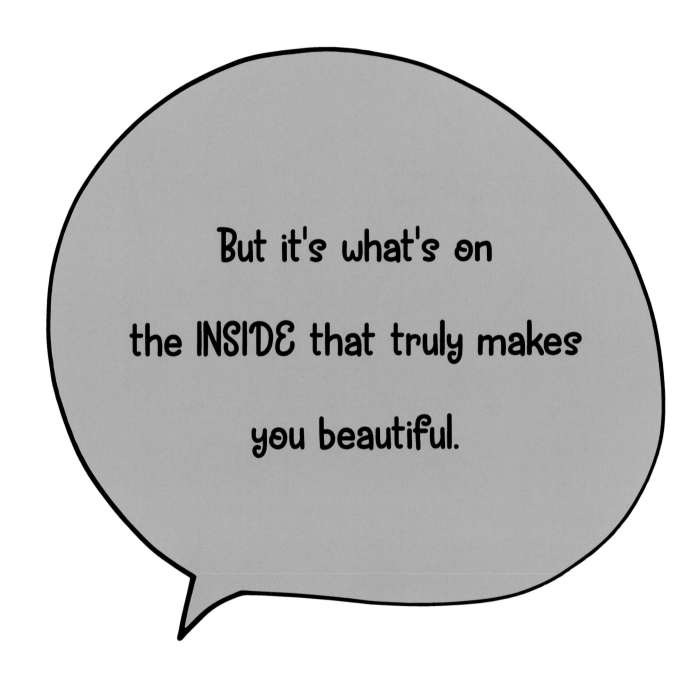

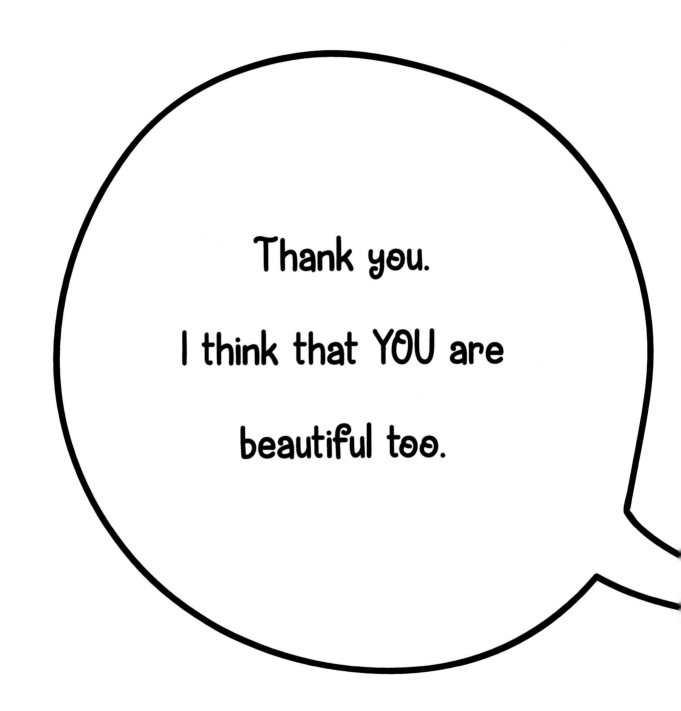

Made in the USA
Coppell, TX
03 June 2022

78415807R00031